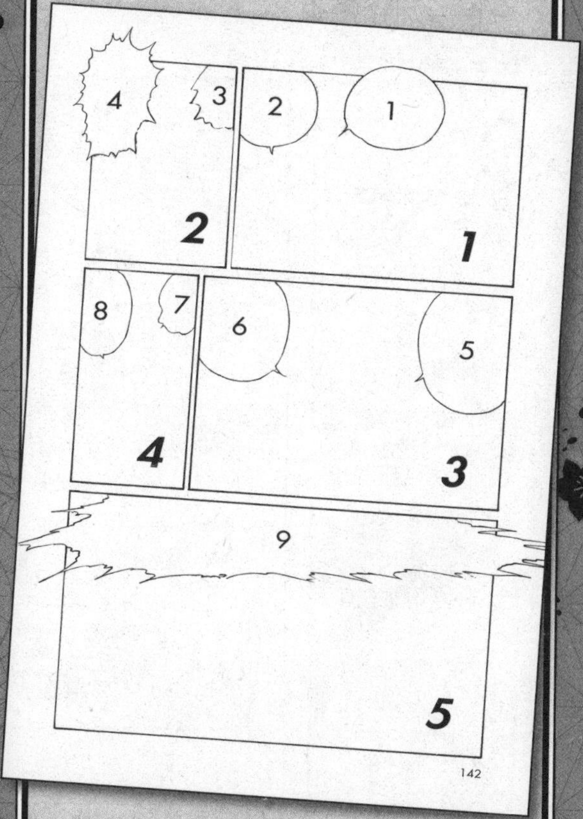

WHERE ARE WE GOING?

HE'S TALL!

SO...?

... ? ?

THE FLASHIEST PLACE IN JAPAN, STEEPED LUST AND AVARICE.

IT'S AN ENTERTAINMENT DISTRICT WHERE DEMONS DWELL.

VOLUME 8—THE STRENGTH OF THE HASHIRA (THE END)

...

YOU GUYS COME WITH ME.

WHAT-EVER.

PAT

HEY!

BUT YOU'D BETTER NOT LET ME DOWN!

?!

HE SURE CAVED EASILY.

TANJIRO ...

HE LET AOI GO.

LET AOI GO!!

PEOPLE HAVE DIFFERENT NEEDS AND ABILITIES! YOU CAN'T JUST USE THEM AS YOU LIKE WITH NO REGARD FOR THEM AT ALL!

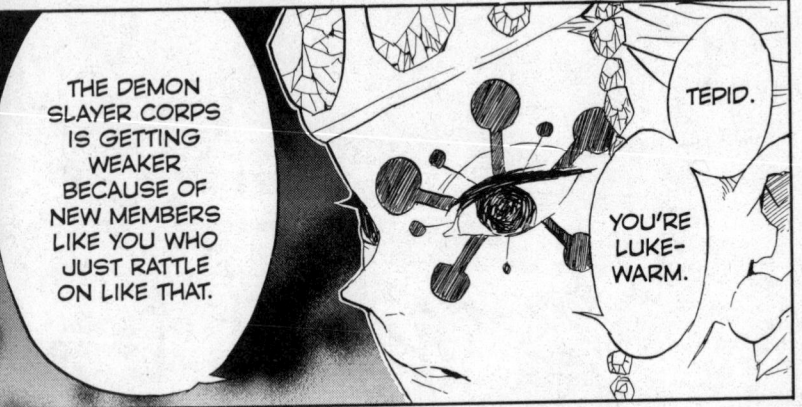

THE DEMON SLAYER CORPS IS GETTING WEAKER BECAUSE OF NEW MEMBERS LIKE YOU WHO JUST RATTLE ON LIKE THAT.

TEPID.

YOU'RE LUKE-WARM.

TAKE ME! I'LL GO IN PLACE OF AOI!

YOU'RE JUST AN UNDERLING! HAS YOUR BRAIN EXPLODED?!

DON'T YOU "HMPH" ME!! SO *WHAT* IF YOU DON'T RECOGNIZE ME?!

SWIK

SHE ISN'T A TSUGUKO, SO I DON'T NEED KOCHO'S PERMISSION!

I NEED A CORPS MEMBER FOR A MISSION, SO I'M TAKING HER!

SWIK

TOSS

THEN I DON'T NEED HER.

SHE ISN'T WEARING A CORPS UNIFORM, IS SHE?!

NAHO ISN'T A CORPS MEMBER!

YANK

DON'T BE SUCH A BORE.

KANAO...

YOU GOT ORDERS EARLIER, DIDN'T YOU?

MISS KANAO...

K...

KANAO!

NAHO
...

COIN...

HASHIRA
...

ORDERS
...

SHINOBU
...

DUTY
...

MISSION
...

AOI...

SUPERIOR
OFFICER
...

KANAO!

"OBEY YOUR HEART!"

COIN...

KANAO!

I'LL TOSS MY COIN TO DECIDE...

GRAAAH!

NE-ZUKO!

NE-ZUKO!

STAGGER

STAGGER

...WAS NOT HAVING TO BE ALONE.

?!

BUTTERFLY MANSION

YAAAH!

AAAAH!

GYAAH!

I'M BEAT.

RETURN-ING FROM A SOLO MISSION

TMP TMP

I...

I SAID...

LET ME GO!

MOST DAYS WE TRAINED, BUT WHEN CROWS CAME WITH INSTRUCTIONS...

GYAAAH!

Do a hundred more!

GRAAAH!

ALMOST FOUR MONTHS HAD PASSED SINCE THE DEATH OF RENGOKU.

I'm gonna die!

...WE TOOK A BREAK AND WENT TO BATTLE DEMONS.

LET'S RUN UNTIL OUR BONES CRUMBLE!

INOSUKE BECAME EVEN MORE RECKLESS THAN BEFORE.

C'MON, GUYS!

GIVE ME A LOCK OF NEZUKO'S HAIR, THEN I'LL FIGHT HARDER!

ZEN STOPPED WHINING, EVEN WHEN HE HAD TO GO ON MISSIONS ALONE.

HFF HFF

JUST A LITTLE FARTHER! HANG IN THERE!

THE BEST THING ABOUT IT...

I CAN'T BE SO SOFT. COME ON!

HUFF

HUFF

...HAVE A FEVER?

IT'S HARD TO BREATHE. DO I...

HUFF

HMM?

IT'S ALL RIGHT, NEZUKO. WE'LL REACH BUTTERFLY MANSION SOON.

SKCH SKCH

KYOJURO!

AAAH...

AHHH...

"...I'LL BE BACK!"

"DON'T WORRY, DAD..."

ALL HE WANTED TO SAY TO YOU WAS...

...PLEASE TAKE CARE OF YOURSELF.

IT'S...

I...

I CAN'T ACCEPT SOMETHING SO PERSONAL.

I'M SURE IT WILL PROTECT YOU.

I WANT YOU TO HAVE IT.

TH-THANK YOU.

...

BE CAREFUL ON YOUR WAY BACK.

I'M GLAD WE GOT TO TALK.

OH, TANJIRO. ONE MORE THING.

HERE...

SHF

THANK YOU.

I'M GLAD TOO.

BOW

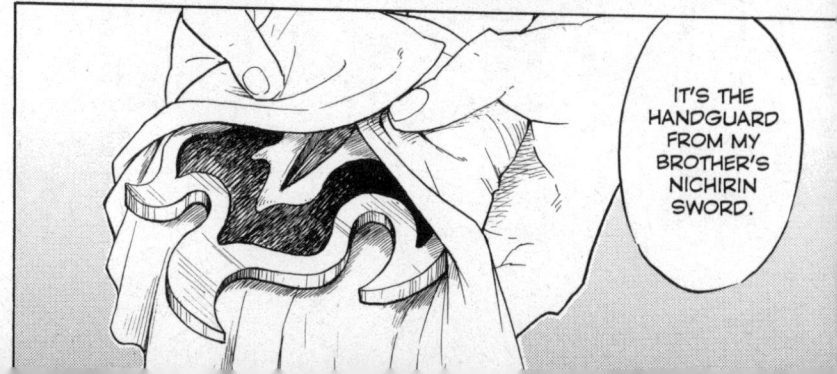

IT'S THE HANDGUARD FROM MY BROTHER'S NICHIRIN SWORD.

IF ANYONE SPEAKS BADLY ABOUT YOU, I'LL HEADBUTT THEM.

PLEASE, WALK THE PATH THAT YOU THINK IS RIGHT.

YOU SHOULDN'T DO THAT.

IF I LEARN SOMETHING, I'LL SEND A CROW.

I'LL ASK FATHER ABOUT THEM.

AND I'LL LOOK FOR THE OTHER BOOKS TOO.

I'LL REPAIR THAT SHREDDED BOOK AS BEST I CAN.

SO I'M GIVING UP BEING...

...A SWORDS-MAN.

A BLOTCH ON THEIR LONG HISTORY.

THIS SEVERS THE SUC-CESSION OF FLAME HASHIRA.

...IN SOME OTHER WAY.

I'LL BE USEFUL...

...MY BROTHER WILL FORGIVE ME.

BUT I'M SURE...

AS HIS BACKUP, I HAD TO BUILD EXPERIENCE.

I WAS SUPPOSED TO BE HIS TSUGUKO.

...MY NICHIRIN SWORD NEVER CHANGED COLOR.

BUT...

NO MATTER HOW HARD I TRAINED...

...I WAS NO GOOD.

PLIP

...THE COLOR DOESN'T CHANGE.

IF YOU DON'T REACH A CERTAIN LEVEL OF SWORDS-MANSHIP...

...A POWERFUL HASHIRA LIKE KYOJURO.

MY BROTHER DIDN'T HAVE A *TSUGUKO*, A SUCCESSOR.

THERE IS NO SHORTCUT.

I'VE BEEN THINKING ABOUT IT FOR A WHILE NOW.

I REALIZE THAT THERE'S NO SUCH METHOD.

THE ONLY OPTION IS TO STRUGGLE ON.

ALL I CAN DO IS MOVE FORWARD...

...NO MATTER HOW DIFFICULT OR FRUS-TRATING IT IS.

...EVENTUALLY I'LL BECOME...

KNCH

AND IF I DO...

THAT'S MY PROBLEM.

MY BODY ISN'T PERFORMING MY TECHNIQUES.

WHEN I USE THE HINOKAMI KAGURA IN A STATE OF TOTAL CONCENTRATION, I CAN'T MOVE THE WAY I WANT.

YOU HAVEN'T?

IF I CONTINUE TO DO CONSTANT, I'LL GET STRONGER DAY BY DAY, BUT I WON'T GET STRONGER INSTANTLY.

TOTAL CONCENTRATION: CONSTANT IMPROVED MY PHYSICAL STRENGTH, BUT THAT'S NOT ENOUGH.

...A WAY TO INSTANTLY GET STRONG ENOUGH TO SAVE RENGOKU.

THAT DAY...

...I WISHED THERE HAD BEEN...

PLEASE, DON'T WORRY ABOUT IT.

THIS ISN'T YOUR FAULT.

NO!

THAT'S ALL RIGHT, BECAUSE NOW I KNOW WHAT TO DO.

...LEARN ANYTHING ABOUT THE HINOKAMI KAGURA OR THE SUN BREATHING MY FATHER MENTIONED.

YOU CAME ALL THE WAY HERE BUT YOU DIDN'T...

I HAVEN'T EVEN MASTERED ALL THE HINOKAMI KAGURA FOR WHICH I DO KNOW THE DANCE MOVEMENTS.

I'LL TRAIN MORE.

IT'S RUINED.

MOST OF IT IS ILLEGIBLE.

THE ANNALS OF THE SUCCESSIVE GENERATIONS OF THE HASHIRA ARE STORED CAREFULLY.

WAS IT ALWAYS LIKE THIS?

I DON'T THINK SO.

I'M SO SORRY.

I THINK FATHER MAY HAVE TORN IT UP HIMSELF.

CHAPTER 69:
MOVE FORWARD—
EVEN IF JUST A LITTLE

SCREW-TYPE HEADBUTT
LESS LETHAL BUT MORE POWERFUL.

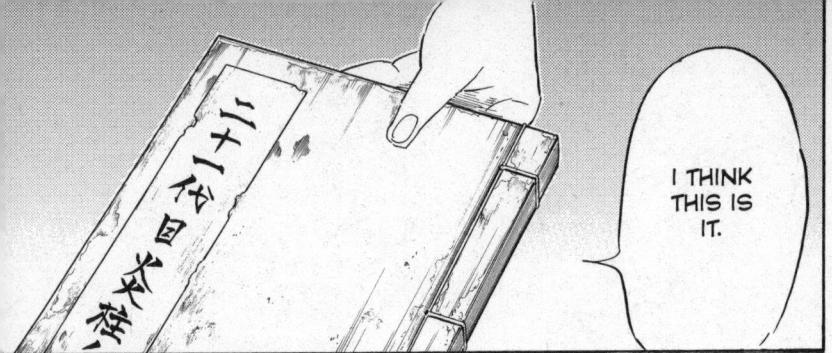

I THINK THIS IS IT.

*BOOK: 21ˢᵀ FLAME HASHIRA

FWUP

THANK YOU.

BOW

IS THIS WHAT YOU WERE HOPING TO FIND?

WHAT IS THIS?!

W...

HE WAS VALIANT TO THE END.

OH... I SEE.

BOW

NOT AT ALL...

I'M JUST SORRY I WASN'T STRONG ENOUGH TO—

THANK YOU VERY MUCH.

I'LL GET THEM. WAIT A MOMENT.

I THINK I KNOW THOSE WRITINGS MY FATHER OFTEN LOOKS AT.

I BET MY BROTHER SAID THAT TOO, RIGHT?

DON'T WORRY ABOUT IT.

...

THANK YOU.

OH.

HUH?

BOW

HE WOKE UP AND WENT OUT TO BUY MORE SAKE.

I THINK HE'S FINE.

WHEN FATHER SPOKE POORLY OF RENGOKU...

...I COULDN'T TALK BACK TO HIM.

I'M RELIEVED.

WHAT WERE MY BROTHER'S FINAL MOMENTS LIKE?

...

GLOOM

NOW I'VE DONE IT...

SORRY. I REALLY HEAD-BUTTED YOUR DAD...

IS HE ALL RIGHT?

OH... THANK YOU.

HAVE SOME TEA.

PLEASE.

TNK

SUN BREATHING... HINOKAMI KAGURA...

NO, INSTEAD OF THAT...

I COME FROM A LONG LINE OF CHARCOAL SELLERS.

WHAT'S THIS ABOUT?

YOU MAY BE A WIELDER OF SUN BREATHING...

...BUT DON'T GET UPPITY, BOY!

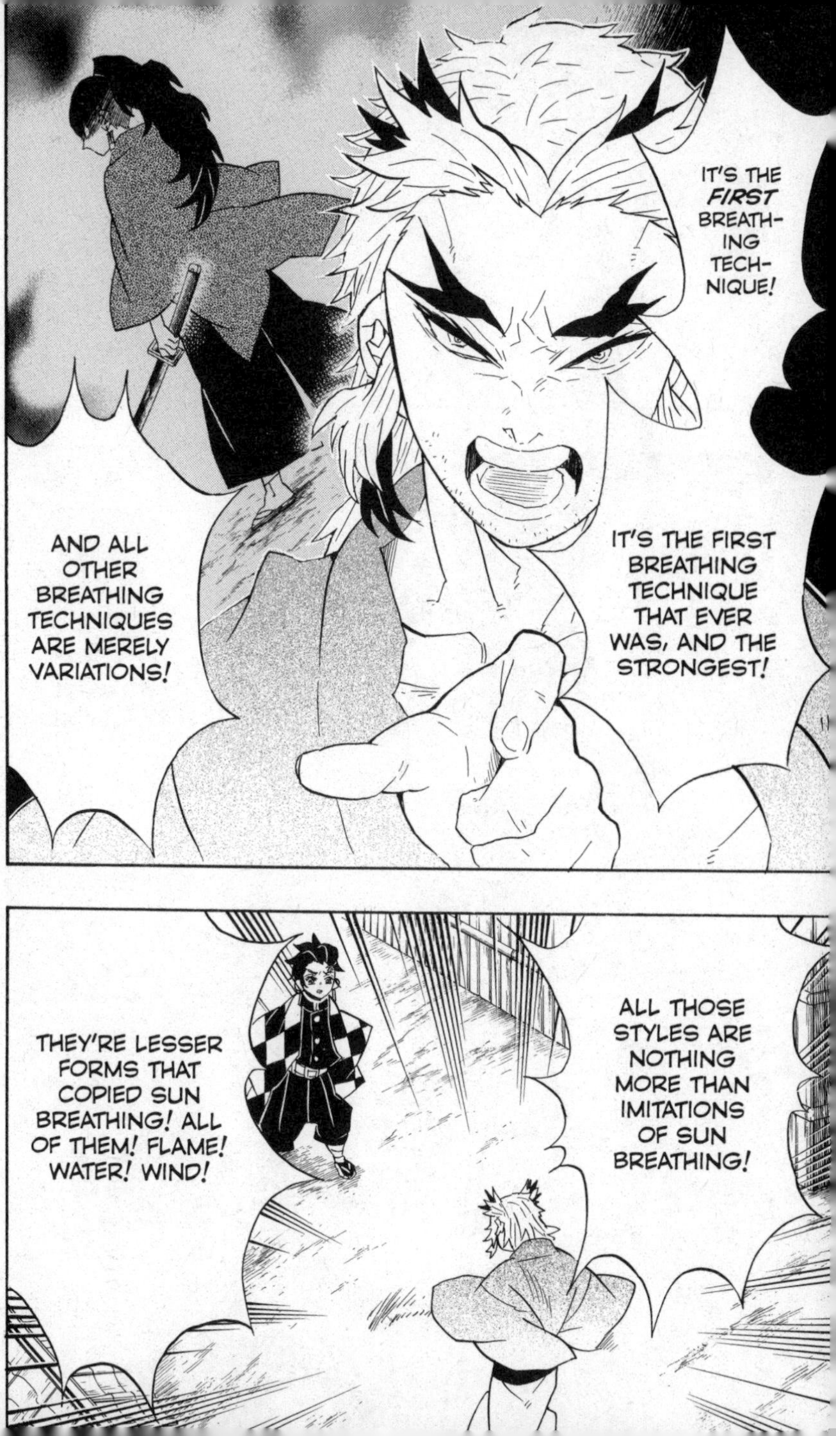

WHY WOULD I DO THAT?! THAT MAKES NO SENSE AT ALL!

ABSOLUTELY NOT!

I KNOW THOSE EAR-RINGS.

YOU'RE A PRAC-TITIONER OF SUN BREATHING.

IT WAS WRITTEN DOWN!

STAGGER

YEAH... SUN BREATHING IS...

DOES SUN BREATHING MEAN THE HINOKAMI KAGURA?

?!

...

IT'S...

?!

YOU...

OH... YOU'RE...

...

YOU PRACTICE THE ART OF *SUN BREATHING*!

YOU DO, DON'T YOU?!

WHAT'S THAT?

SUN BREATH-ING?

THE FUNERAL IS OVER!

STOP LOOKING SO MISERABLE!

SENJURO!

HEY!

PLEASE, DON'T SAY THAT!

WHAT A HORRIBLE THING TO SAY!

A PERSON'S CAPABILITIES AND LIMITATIONS ARE SET AT BIRTH.

THEY'RE DUST! OF NO VALUE!

...THE REST ARE JUST RABBLE!

A RARE FEW ENTER THE WORLD WITH TALENT...

HE HAD NO TALENT, SO *OF COURSE* HE DIED!

THAT'S HOW IT WAS WITH KYOJURO! WORTHLESS!

CHAPTER 68: WIELDER

HE ENTRUSTED ME WITH MESSAGES FOR HIS FATHER AND BROTHER.

HAVE YOU HEARD THE SAD NEWS ABOUT KYOJURO RENGOKU?

UM...

ARE YOU ALL RIGHT? YOU'RE VERY PALE.

I HEARD WHAT HAPPENED TO HIM, BUT...

...

FROM MY BROTHER?

I BET HIS LAST WORDS WERE WORTHLESS ANYWAY!

STOP!

...RIGHT?

YOU MUST BE SENJURO...

BOW

!

HUFF

HUFF

HUFF

HUFF

IT'S GUIDING ME BASED ON RENGOKU'S LAST WISHES.

HUFF

HUFF

HUFF

RENGOKU'S CROW...

THANK YOU...

HUFF

HUFF

HUFF

HE WAS TRAINING EVEN THOUGH HIS WOUNDS HAVEN'T HEALED YET, AND SHINOBU WAS LIVID!

WAAAH

I'M FINE, I'M FINE.

HA HA HA!

I'M REALLY SORRY!

SHE ORDERED HIM TO REST, BUT...

TANJIRO ISN'T ANYWHERE TO BE FOUND!

...AND HE WENT OFF SOMEWHERE LIKE THAT?!

HIS STOMACH WOUND WAS REALLY DEEP...

IS HE CRAZY?!

WAAAAH GYAAAAH

PEOPLE DON'T SIMPLY RECOVER INSTANTLY.

EVEN INOSUKE WAS WAILING.

HE MUST HAVE BEEN SO FRUSTRATED.

YOU MUST ROUSE YOUR ACHING HEART AND STAND BACK UP.

NO MATTER HOW STRONG SOMEONE IS, THEY CAN FEEL PAIN AND SADNESS.

BUT HIDING FROM IT DOESN'T SOLVE ANYTHING.

HE WAS A LITTLE WEIRD, BUT HE WAS STRONG.

HE HAD THAT WAY ABOUT HIM.

I'M SURE RENGOKU WAS THAT KIND OF PERSON.

BUTTERFLY MANSION

SOMETIMES HE GETS IT IN HIS HEAD THAT A THING IS IMPOSSIBLE.

EVEN TANJIRO IS DEPRESSED.

IT'S SAD.

...DIES...

THAT'S UNDERSTAND-ABLE. I MEAN, WHEN EVEN SOMEONE AS WELL TRAINED AS RENGOKU ...

...THEN UPPER RANK 3 HAS INDEED FALLEN.

IF YOU TOOK A BLOW FROM A SWORDSMAN WHO ISN'T EVEN A HASHIRA...

LEAVE ME.

TWITCH

I WILL CONTINUE SEARCHING TO FIND THE ANSWERS YOU SEEK.
AS YOU COMMANDED, I KILLED ONE OF THE HASHIRA. ALL IS WELL.
AZAKA, YOU APPEAR TO BE UNDER...
...A MISCONCEPTION.
VMM
RAK

...AS QUICKLY AS POSSIBLE.

I'M HAVING MY COMPANY CREATE A SPECIAL MEDICATION FOR HIM...

HWOOO

I'VE COME TO REPORT...

OH MY! HE SEEMS TO BE VERY INTELLIGENT.

EVEN WITHOUT A BLOOD CONNECTION, WE ARE AS CLOSE AS ANY BIOLOGICAL PARENT AND CHILD COULD BE. HE'LL CARRY ON FOR ME WHEN I'M GONE.

NOT HAVING BEEN BLESSED WITH CHILDREN, I WAS DEPRESSED. BUT I FEEL SO MUCH BETTER NOW THAT THIS MARVELOUS CHILD HAS ARRIVED.

OH DEAR! HOW SAD!

HE CANNOT GO OUTSIDE IN THE DAYLIGHT.

BUT HE HAS A CHRONIC SKIN DISEASE.

CHAPTER 67:
LOOKING FOR SOMETHING

NOT ONE OF THE PASSENGERS DIED?
KYOJURO STRUGGLED VALIANTLY. HE WAS AN INCREDIBLE YOUNG MAN.

I AM NOT FORLORN.
I CANNOT LIVE MUCH LONGER.
SOON, I WILL GO TO THE OTHER WORLD WHERE KYOJURO AND THE REST ARE.

I WILL ANNIHILATE ALL DEMONS.

OH?

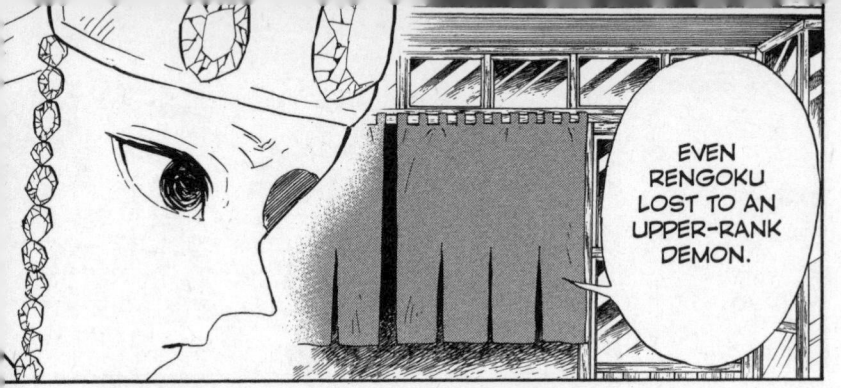

EVEN RENGOKU LOST TO AN UPPER-RANK DEMON.

I CAN'T BELIEVE IT.

NAMU AMIDA BUTSU...

FAREWELL
...

... RENGOKU.

WAAAAH

PIF POF

NEWS OF RENGOKU'S DEATH SOON REACHED UBUYASHIKI AND THE HASHIRA.

YOU *CAN* OR YOU *CAN'T*! IT DOESN'T DO YOU ANY GOOD TO SIT THERE WONDERING ABOUT THE *MAYBES*!

...SO DON'T WORRY ABOUT ANYTHING OTHER THAN LIVING UP TO THAT!

HE SAID HE BELIEVED IN US...

CRYING WON'T BRING ANY OF THEM BACK!

EVERY-THING THAT DIES RETURNS TO THE EARTH...

THIS IS ALL SO FRUSTRATING.

EVERY TIME I LEARN TO DO SOMETHING NEW...

...I LEARN JUST HOW MUCH MORE THERE IS I DON'T KNOW.

...AND I'M STILL SO FAR BEHIND THEM.

THESE AWESOME PEOPLE ARE FIGHTING WITH SUCH SKILL AND POWER...

CAN I...

...

I FEEL LIKE I'M FALLING BEHIND.

I KNOW HE DID.

WAS THERE REALLY AN UPPER-RANK DEMON?

I CAN'T BELIEVE...

...HE'S DEAD.

YES.

WHY DID IT COME HERE?

WAS IT THAT STRONG?

YES.

...TO MINIMIZE THE DAMAGE TO THE TRAIN CARS.

...RENGOKU USED A BUNCH OF TECHNIQUES...

WHEN THE TRAIN WENT OFF THE TRACKS...

YOU DID SPLENDIDLY.

MOTHER...

DID I USE MY GIFTS WISELY?

...DID I DO WELL?

I'M A HASHIRA.

IT'S MY JOB TO SHIELD YOU JUNIOR MEMBERS.

DON'T WORRY OVER MY DEATH.

TANJIRO...

...THE YOUNG BUDS TO BE PLUCKED.

ANY HASHIRA WOULD DO THE SAME. WE CAN'T ALLOW...

BOAR-HEAD BOY...

STAND TALL AND BE PROUD.

...KEEP YOUR HEART BURNING, GRIT YOUR TEETH AND MOVE FORWARD.

NO MATTER HOW WEAK OR UNWORTHY YOU FEEL...

IT WON'T STOP FOR YOU WHILE YOU WALLOW IN GRIEF.

IF YOU JUST CURL UP IN A BALL AND HIDE, TIME WILL PASS YOU BY.

...TANJIRO...

...I BELIEVE IN YOUR LITTLE SISTER.

I CONSIDER HER A MEMBER OF THE DEMON SLAYER CORPS.

...SHED HER OWN BLOOD TO PROTECT HUMANS.

ON THE TRAIN, I SAW HER...

...SHE'S A MEMBER OF THE CORPS, NO MATTER WHAT ANYONE SAYS!

IF SHE RISKS HER LIFE TO FIGHT DEMONS AND PROTECT PEOPLE...

NO.

I'M GOING TO DIE SOON.

BUT I HAVE SOMETHING TO SAY, SO LISTEN.

ISN'T THERE ANY WAY TO STOP YOUR BLEEDING?

CAN'T YOU USE YOUR BREATH-ING?

P-PLEASE...

RENGOKU...

THAT'S ENOUGH.

...TO TAKE THE PATH THAT HE THINKS IS RIGHT, TO FOLLOW HIS HEART.

...MY LITTLE BROTHER SENJURO...

I WANT YOU TO TELL...

AND...

...MY FATHER TO TAKE CARE OF HIMSELF.

AND TELL...

...TO VISIT HOUSE RENGOKU, WHERE I WAS BORN.

YOU SHOULD GO...

MY FATHER READ THEM OFTEN, BUT I DIDN'T...

...SO I HAVE NO IDEA WHAT'S IN THEM.

THERE YOU'LL FIND THE WRITINGS OF PAST FLAME HASHIRA.

THEY MAY CONTAIN RECORDS OF THE HINOKAMI KAGURA YOU MENTIONED.

BLRT

CHAPTER 66:
SCATTERING INTO DAWN

...

...IN MY VISIONS OF THE PAST.

I REMEMBER SOMETHING I SAW...

YOU'RE HURT PRETTY BAD TOO, Y'KNOW.

THAT CUT IN YOUR BELLY WILL OPEN UP.

AND IF YOU DIE, I WON'T HAVE MY VICTORY ANYMORE.

LET'S TALK A LITTLE HERE AT THE END.

COME HERE.

DON'T CRY SO HARD, KID...

HE DIDN'T LET ANYONE DIE!

...THAT YOU HAVEN'T WON TODAY! RENGOKU HASN'T LOST!

RENGOKU IS STRONGER— MUCH STRONGER THAN YOU!

HE PROTECTED THE REST OF US!

HE SAW THE FIGHT THROUGH TO THE END!

...BELONGS TO RENGOKU!

AND THE VICTORY...

THIS IS *YOUR* DEFEAT!

HFF

HFF

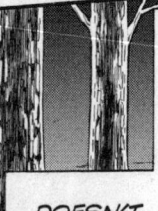

I'M NOT RUNNING FROM THE DEMON SLAYER CORPS—I'M RUNNING FROM THE SUN!

WHAT IS THAT BRAT TALKING ABOUT?

DOESN'T HE HAVE ANY BRAINS IN HIS HEAD?

SOON HE'LL RUN OUT OF STRENGTH AND DIE!

BESIDES, THIS FIGHT IS ALREADY OVER.

...!

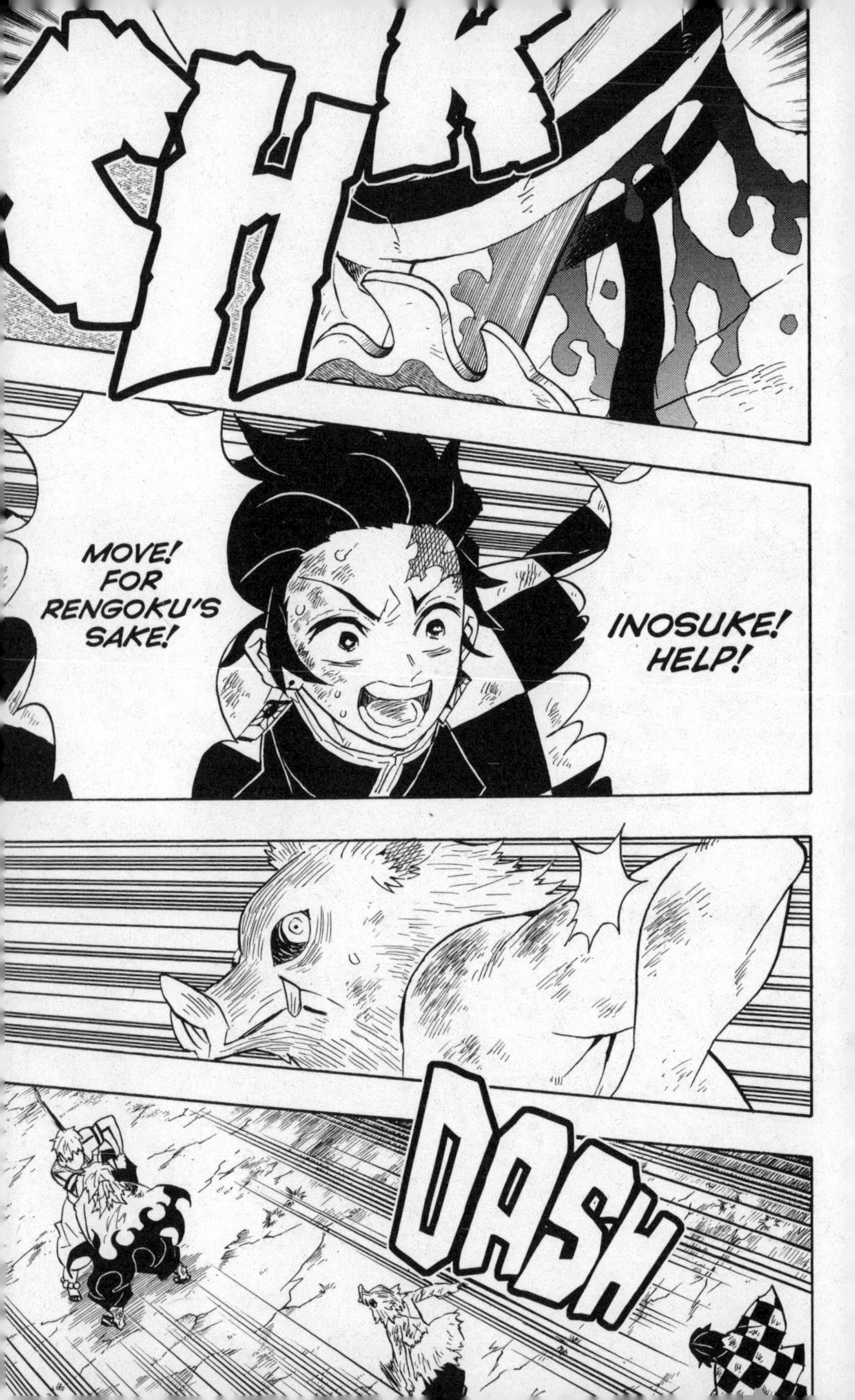
INOSUKE! HELP!
MOVE! FOR RENGOKU'S SAKE!
DASH

CHAPTER 65: WHOSE VICTORY?

HE CAN STILL SWING A SWORD?!

GAGH!

...TO HAVE HAD *YOU* AS MY MOTHER!

THE HONOR IS MINE...

YOU'RE ONE OF THE CHOSEN STRONG ONES!

KYOJURO...

YES, MOTHER?

...MY NEXT QUESTION.

THINK HARD ABOUT...

I WON'T LET ANYONE HERE DIE!

I WILL FULFILL MY DUTY!

ESOTERIC ART!

FLAME BREATH-ING

...I'LL SLASH UP A BROAD AREA!

IN AN INSTANT...

NO MATTER HOW HARD THEY STRUGGLE, HUMANS CANNOT DEFEAT DEMONS.

IT MAY BE BECAUSE I'M WOUNDED, BUT THIS HAPPENS WHEN I USE HINOKAMI KAGURA.

MY LIMBS HAVE NO STRENGTH.

EVEN THOUGH I WANT TO HELP!

MPH

MM

TWCH

SKCH

HN O O

NO MATTER HOW DESPERATELY YOU FIGHT, KYOJURO, IT'S ALL USELESS.

THAT WONDERFUL CUT YOU MADE HAS ALREADY HEALED COMPLETELY.

IF YOU WERE A DEMON, YOU WOULD HEAL IN THE BLINK OF AN EYE.

TO A DEMON, THOSE ARE JUST SCRATCHES.

YOUR LEFT EYE IS CRUSHED. YOUR RIBS ARE BROKEN. YOU'RE BLEEDING INSIDE.

THOSE ARE SERIOUS WOUNDS.

BUT WHAT ABOUT YOU?

RENGOKU!

RENGOKU...

RENGOKU...

THERE'S NO OPENING. I CAN'T GET IN. I CAN'T KEEP UP WITH THEIR MOVEMENTS.

I FEEL IT. IF I GET TOO CLOSE, THERE IS ONLY DEATH.

IT'S LIKE THEY'RE IN ANOTHER DIMENSION.

I KNOW THAT IF I GO IN TO HELP, I'LL ONLY GET IN THE WAY.

TREMBLE

SHAKE

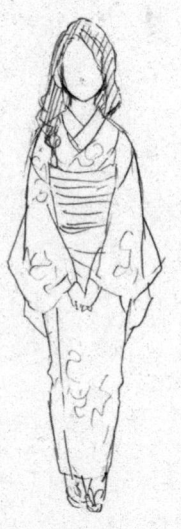

STILL, NONE ACCEPTED MY PROPOSAL.

THE OTHER HASHIRA I'VE KILLED...

...DIDN'T HAVE FLAMES.

ONE CANNOT SIMPLY *DECIDE* TO BECOME A DEMON. YOU MUST BE CHOSEN.

WHY IS THAT?

AS SOMEONE WHO ALSO WALKS THE PATH OF THE WARRIOR, I DO NOT UNDERSTAND IT.

I AM AKAZA.

LET ME TELL YOU, KYOJURO, WHY YOUR POWER WILL NEVER TRULY REACH PERFECTION.

I AM THE FLAME HASHIRA KYOJURO RENGOKU.

BECAUSE YOU AGE. BECAUSE EVENTUALLY YOU'LL DIE.

IT'S BECAUSE YOU'RE *HUMAN*.

...YOU CAN TRAIN FOR HUNDREDS OF YEARS AND KEEP GETTING STRONGER.

IF YOU DO...

BECOME A DEMON, KYOJURO.

WHAT ARE WE GOING TO TALK ABOUT?

I THOUGHT HE MIGHT INTERRUPT THE CONVER-SATION...

...WE'RE ABOUT TO HAVE.

THIS IS OUR FIRST MEETING, BUT I ALREADY HATE YOU.

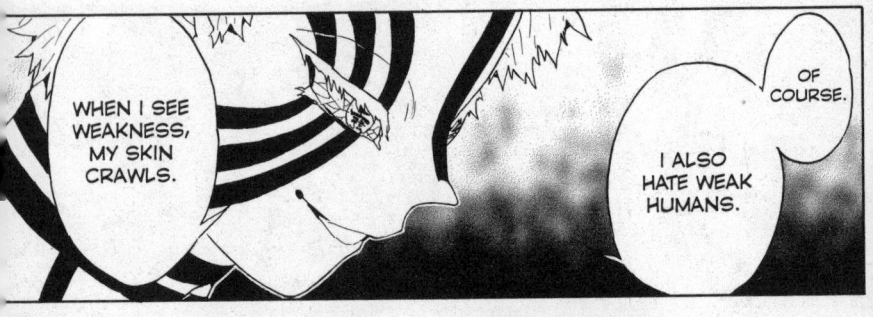

WHEN I SEE WEAKNESS, MY SKIN CRAWLS.

OF COURSE.

I ALSO HATE WEAK HUMANS.

THEN I HAVE A GREAT IDEA...

AHA...

YOU AND I HAVE VERY DIFFERENT VALUES.

NICE KATANA.

NOW WHY WOULD SOMEONE AS POWERFUL AS YOU ATTACK THE WOUNDED FIRST?

FAST REGENERATION AND AN OVERWHELMING DEMON AURA. HE MUST BE...

...AN UPPER-RANK DEMON.

*EYES: UPPER 3

The moment Inosuke rams the train.

...BUT YOU'LL BE MUCH STRONGER THAN YOU WERE YESTERDAY.

THERE'RE LOTS OF THINGS YOU CAN DO IF YOU CAN MASTER YOUR BREATHING.

THAT DOESN'T MEAN YOU CAN DO *ANYTHING*...

...

YEAH.

A LOT OF INJURIES, BUT NO DEATHS. NO NEED FOR YOU TO OVERDO IT.

EVERY-ONE'S SAFE!

TAP

CONCENTRATE.

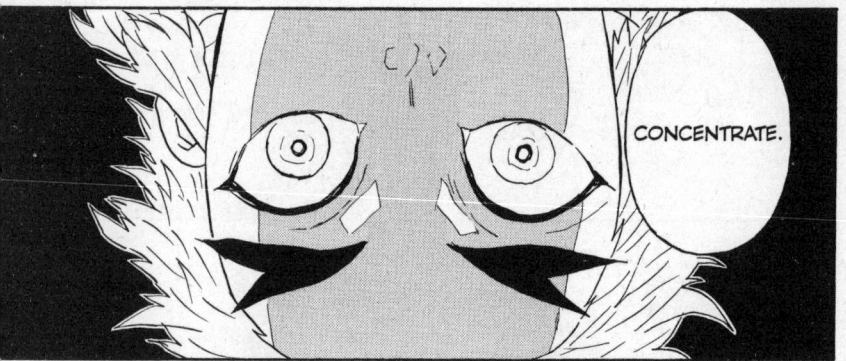

PANT   GASP

?

HUFF

HVNNG

NO MORE BLEEDING.

THAT'S IT.

HEMO-
STASIS.

STOP THE
BLEEDING.

THAT'S
IT...

MMPH

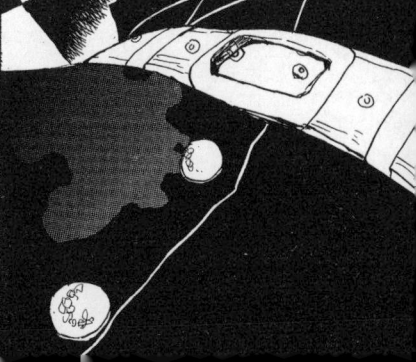

YOUR STOMACH IS BLEEDING.

I'LL DO MY BEST.

BUT THAT'S JUST THE FIRST OF 10,000 STEPS YET TO COME!

FOCUS ON EVERY INCH OF YOUR BODY.

CONCENTRATE MORE. IMPROVE THE ACCURACY OF YOUR BREATH.

BROKEN BLOOD VESSELS.

THERE ARE BLOOD VESSELS.

HFF

HFF

HFF

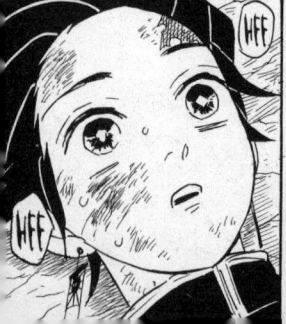
HFF

CONCENTRATE MORE.

HFF

HFF

WHAT A PATHETIC...

...MARE.

...NIGHT...

I'M IMPRESSED!

IT LOOKS LIKE YOU CAN DO TOTAL CONCENTRATION: CONSTANT!

THAT'S THE FIRST STEP TO BECOMING A HASHIRA!

REN-GOKU...

THE UPPER-RANK DEMONS...

THEY'VE BURIED MOUNTAINS OF SLAYERS—EVEN PUT HASHIRA IN THEIR GRAVES.

THEIR RANKS HAVEN'T CHANGED FOR A HUNDRED YEARS.

IT'S ALWAYS US LOWER-LEVEL DEMONS THAT THE DEMON SLAYERS KILL.

THEIR STRENGTH IS OUT OF THIS WORLD.

GLOP

I WANT ANOTHER SHOT! I WANT TO DO IT OVER!

GLUP

EVEN AFTER RECEIVING THAT MUCH BLOOD, I STILL COULDN'T MATCH THE UPPER RANKS.

*EYE: LOWER 1

RENGOKU
...

THEY'VE GOT TO BE SAFE!

NEZUKO, ZENITSU
...

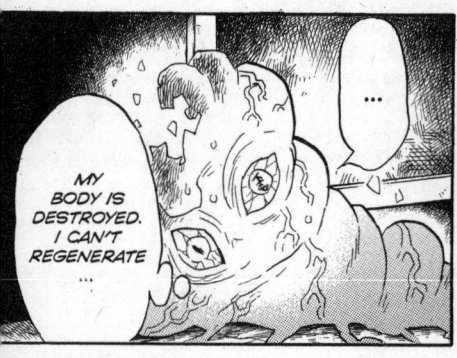

...

MY BODY IS DESTROYED. I CAN'T REGENERATE ...

HFF

HFF

HFF

RIDICULOUS!

'THAT'S RIDICULOUS!

DID I LOSE?

AM I GOING TO DIE? ME?!

BOW

...

PLEASE.

NO, HE'S ALREADY SUFFERED ENOUGH.

...TO MAKE MY UNDERLING HAPPY.

HMPH! BECAUSE I'M A GOOD BOSS, I'LL DO IT...

HELP HIM.

YOU DON'T HAVE TO DO THAT...

BUT AFTER I HELP HIM, I'M RIPPING OUT ALL HIS HAIR!

SNORT

I'VE GOT TO GET MY BREATHING UNDER CONTROL...

I HAVE TO HELP THE INJURED...

HUFF

HUFF

DAWN IS COMING.

ARE YOU ALL RIGHT?
SAN-TARO!
HANG IN THERE!
FLMP
THE DEMON'S FLESH WAS SPRINGY AND THAT SAVED ME!
WEIRD, HUH?

CHAPTER 62: ENDING IN A DREAM

CONTENTS

THE STRENGTH OF THE HASHIRA

INOSUKE HASHIBIRA

He also went through Final Selection at the same time as Tanjiro. He wears the pelt of a wild boar and is very belligerent.

ZENITSU AGATSUMA

He went through Final Selection at the same time as Tanjiro. He's usually cowardly, but when he falls asleep his true power comes out.

GIYU TOMIOKA

The Hashira who invited Tanjiro to join the Demon Slayer Corps.

KYOJURO RENGOKU

A Hashira in the Demon Slayer Corps. He annihilates demons with Flame Breathing.

KANAO TSUYURI

Successor to Shinobu. She doesn't talk much and has difficulty making any kind of decision by herself.

SHINOBU KOCHO

Another Hashira in the Demon Slayer Corps. Familiar with pharmacology, she is a swordswoman who has created a poison that kills demons.

LOWER RANK 1: ENMU

One of the Twelve Kizuki. He's infatuated with Kibutsuji, and when he gains new strength, he targets Tanjiro and the Hashira.

MUZAN KIBUTSUJI

Kibutsuji turned Nezuko into a demon. He is Tanjiro's enemy and hides his nature in order to live among human beings.

CHARACTERS

TANJIRO KAMADO

A kind boy who saved his sister and now aims to avenge his family. He can smell the scent of demons and an opponent's weakness.

Tanjiro's younger sister. A demon attacked her and turned her into a demon. But unlike other demons, she fights her urges and tries to protect Tanjiro.

NEZUKO KAMADO

STORY

In Taisho-era Japan, young Tanjiro makes a living selling charcoal. One day, demons kill his family and turn his younger sister Nezuko into a demon. Tanjiro and Nezuko set out to find a way to return Nezuko to human form and defeat Kibutsuji, the demon who killed their family!

After joining the Demon Slayer Corps, Tanjiro meets Tamayo and Yushiro—demons who oppose Kibutsuji—who provide a clue to how Nezuko may regain her humanity. On a new mission, Tanjiro boards a steam train and joins up with Rengoku, the Flame Hashira. Meanwhile, Enmu, a lower-ranked demon who has gained new powers, tries to use dreams to kill Tanjiro and the others. Awakening from his dream, Tanjiro presses Enmu hard, but...

DEMON SLAYER
KIMETSU NO YAIBA

**THE STRENGTH
OF THE HASHIRA**

KOYOHARU
GOTOUGE

**DEMON SLAYER:
KIMETSU NO YAIBA
VOLUME 8**
Shonen Jump Edition

Story and Art by
KOYOHARU GOTOUGE

KIMETSU NO YAIBA
© 2016 by Koyoharu Gotouge
All rights reserved. First published in Japan
in 2016 by SHUEISHA Inc., Tokyo. English
translation rights arranged by SHUEISHA Inc.

TRANSLATION John Werry
ENGLISH ADAPTATION Stan!
TOUCH-UP ART & LETTERING John Hunt
DESIGN Adam Grano
EDITOR Mike Montesa

Published by VIZ Media, LLC
P.O. Box 77010
San Francisco, CA 94107

10
First printing, September 2019
Tenth printing, November 2021

PARENTAL ADVISORY
DEMON SLAYER: KIMETSU NO YAIBA is rated T for
Teen and recommended for ages 13 and up. This
volume contains realistic and fantasy violence.

VIZ MEDIA
viz.com

SHONEN JUMP

Gratitude

KOYOHARU GOTOUGE

Hello! I'm Gotouge. How have you all been? Money can't buy health, so I pray from the bottom of my heart that you're all healthy and active. Thank you for all the best wishes, snacks, tea and handmade goods you send. I'm in such a state of great excitement every day that it makes my nose bleed. When I get a bloody nose, I just stuff in tissues and wear a mask over it all, so I'm fine.